Reading 5–6

Author: Stephanie Cooper
Illustrators: Emma Holt and Chris McGhie

How to use this book

Look out for these features!

IN THE ACTIVITIES

The parents' notes at the top of each activity will give you:
► a simple explanation about what your child is learning
► an idea of how you can work with your child on the activity.

This small page number guides you to the back of the book, where you will find further ideas for help.

These magic stars provide useful facts and helpful hints!

AT THE BACK OF THE BOOK

Every activity has a section for parents containing:
► further explanations about what the activity teaches
► games that can be easily recreated at home
► questions to ask your child to encourage their learning
► tips on varying the activity if it seems too easy or too difficult for your child.

You will also find the answers at the back of the book.

HELPING YOUR CHILD AS THEY USE THIS BOOK

Why not try starting at the beginning of the book and work through it? Your child should only attempt one activity at a time. Remember, it is best to learn little and often when we are feeling wide awake!

EQUIPMENT YOUR CHILD WILL NEED

► a pencil for writing
► an eraser for correcting mistakes
► coloured pencils for drawing and colouring in.

You might also like to have ready some spare paper and some collections of objects (for instance, small toys, Lego bricks, buttons...) for some of the activities.

Contents

Is it a question?

Read each sentence, then write a full stop or a question mark at the end of each one.

? .

1. What day is it today ☐

2. Can I borrow your pencil ☐

3. I can come to your party ☐

4. Why can't you come out to play ☐

5. Who did you say your brother was ☐

6. Sorry ☐

This activity will help your child to identify when a
sentence is a question and to learn to use question marks.

Ask them to read each sentence with the correct intonation.

Parents

44

7. Pardon, could you repeat that ☐

8. When can you come to the park ☐

9. When we get to school we will see
   our friends ☐

10. How are you ☐

11. When we go outside, do you want
    to play football ☐

12. Do you want to go swimming ☐

Reading numbers

Bill Blastoff has to count from twenty down to zero for the space shuttle to take off. Write the number words in the right order so he can read them.

sixteen

one

fifteen

ten

eight

eighteen

twenty

eleven

zero

nineteen

four

seventeen

three

twelve

two

nine

six

fourteen

thirteen

five

seven

twenty

fifteen

seven

▷ This activity will help your child learn how to read numbers to twenty.

▷ Point out the similarity in the 'teen' endings of some of the numbers.

Reading colours

Look at the colour words in the border. Colour them

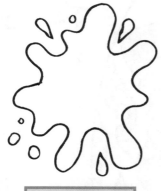

green

black

pink

Colour the pictures. Then write
colour labels for each one.

1. black and white   2. _____

3. _____   4. _____

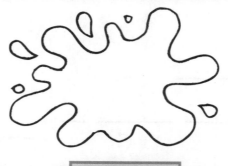

white

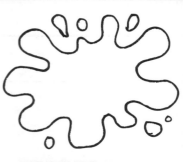

orange

blue

This activity will help your child to read colour words.

Ask them to colour in the space above each colour word in the border first.

44

5. _____   6. _____

brown

7. _____   8. _____

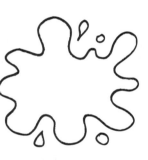

purple

9. _____   10. _____

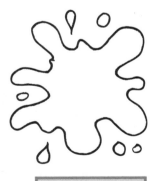

red

yellow

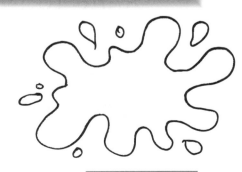

grey

9

Questions and answers

Answer some questions about Mehreen's week.

Monday	Swimming at school, Brownies.
Tuesday	Piano lesson (Dad taking me).
Wednesday	Mum's and Dad's tenth wedding anniversary party, at six o'clock.
Thursday	After-school club with Rachel.
Friday	Going to Nan's and Grandad's house in Liverpool for the weekend.
Saturday	Go to the park with Nan.
Sunday	Back home.

This activity will help your child to understand the days of the week, and to search a text for answers.

Parents

44

1. Where is Mehreen going on Friday?

_____

2. Who is taking her to her piano lesson on Tuesday?

_____

3. Where does she go on Monday?

_____

4. What is the party for on Wednesday?

_____

5. Who goes with Mehreen to the after-school club on Thursday?

_____

6. When will Mehreen go home from her Nan and Grandad's?

_____

7. When will she go to the park?

_____

8. If it is Monday, how many days are there until she goes to Liverpool?

_____

Reading labels

Look around this town.

This activity will help your child learn how to find words that give information.

When they answer the questions, encourage them to give a detailed verbal answer before writing it down.

Parents

44

Now answer these questions.

1. Where is the village hall?

_____

_____

_____

2. What is on Park Road?

_____

_____

_____

3. Where is the cinema?

_____

_____

_____

4. Where are the zebra crossings?

_____

_____

_____

Book covers

Read these two covers.

Another exciting adventure for Dan the digging dog. This time, he digs his way to Australia on the other side of the world to meet up with his old friend, Don, the barking dog. Dan and Don bark and dig their way to New Zealand meeting all sorts of strange animals on the way, including Karl the talking kangaroo.

G'day sport!

AUSTRALIA

Arf, arf!

Digger Dan

Write down what you think the book is about. Continue on some spare paper, if you wish.

_____

_____

_____

▶ This activity will help your child to read the title, pictures and blurb of an unfamiliar book.

▶ Talk about the covers first, then ask them to write about each book's contents.

One hundred new songs, all about space, including Sing a song of spaceman, Jack and Jill went to the moon, Humpty Dumpty sat on the rocket, Little Miss Muffet sat on planet Jupiter and Old King Cole was a merry old spaceman. With music for recorders and piano.

100 SPACE SONGS

100 SPACE SONGS

Write down what the book is about.

_____

_____

_____

Make a book cover

Look at this page from a book about
how to grow seeds at home.

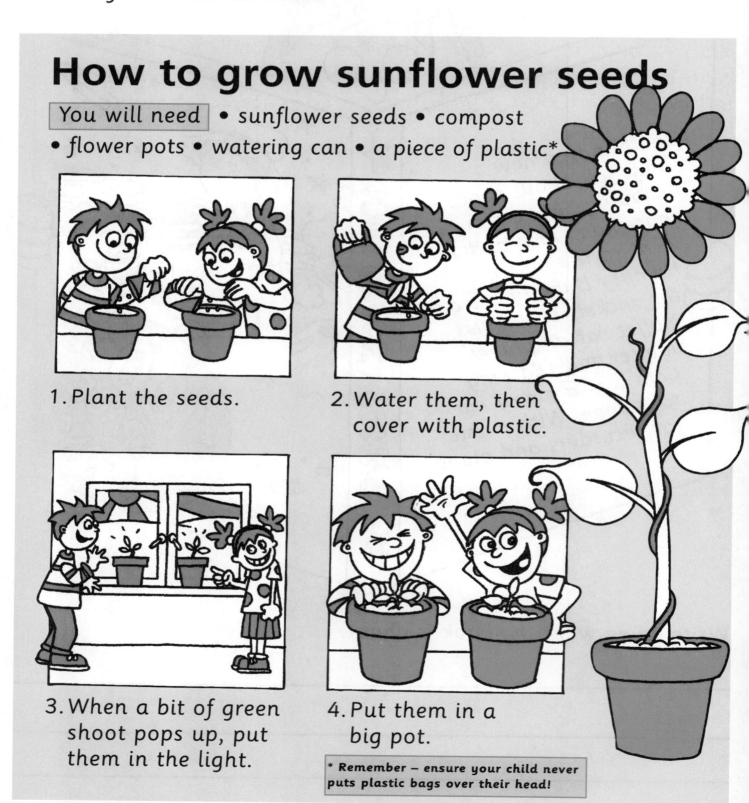

How to grow sunflower seeds

You will need • sunflower seeds • compost
• flower pots • watering can • a piece of plastic*

1. Plant the seeds.

2. Water them, then cover with plastic.

3. When a bit of green shoot pops up, put them in the light.

4. Put them in a big pot.

* Remember – ensure your child never puts plastic bags over their head!

Now draw your own front and back cover. What is your book about?

Don't forget to include the title, the blurb and an illustration!

Reading part of a story

Read these two stories.

1. It was night time and Max the Monster was creeping around the house. He was looking for someone to scare. He didn't see Molly Mouse slipping out of her mouse hole. "I'm tired of Max scaring everyone," she thought. So she took a big breath and shouted, "Boo!" Max was so shocked that he stood still and started to cry.

How do you think Max feels? Use the words in the box to help.

_____

_____

_____

This activity will help your child to make sense of pictures and words they read to describe a story incident.

Ask them to say and then write about what is happening now, and to describe what each character is feeling. Read the clue words to help them.

Parents

45

2. The two ugly sisters and their mother left Cinderella behind and went to the Prince's party at the palace. Cinderella could hear her sisters laughing at her as they went. "They are so unkind," she thought, as a little tear fell onto her cheek.

How do you think Cinderella feels?

_____

_____

_____

Reading stories

Read these stories. Which do you like the most, and which do you like the least? Why?

1. At night, I imagine that I'm looking out through the window of my space shuttle. I'm the very first person to travel to Mars. When I get there, I'm shocked because there is an airport with a sign saying 'Welcome to Mars', and a little green man asks me if he can please see my passport.

I like/don't like this story because:_____

_____

_____

► This activity will help your child to learn how to read different stories and to compare and contrast them.

► Ask them to say, then write, what they do and don't like about each story.

Parents

45

2. The rabbits were frightened. They sat in their burrow, but just outside was Fred Fox, and he wanted to eat them. Fred's face peered in. "I'm too big to come in and get you," he said. "But I'm going to go and get Ted Fox who is smaller than I am." Fred Fox crept away and the rabbits were safe. But they knew the foxes would come back.

I like/don't like this story because: _____

_____

_____

_____

21

Make a choice

Read these stories. Which one do you prefer and why?

1. Dino the dinosaur thought he was the biggest dinosaur in Dinoland. He had the sharpest claws, the sharpest teeth and the loudest roar. One day, he went to the water hole for a drink. As he drank, he saw two new tree trunks nearby. Suddenly the two trees started to roar. Dino looked up, and up, and up. They weren't tree trunks, they were the legs of a hipposaur. The hipposaur bent down. "He's going to gobble me up," thought Dino. Then, suddenly, the hipposaur stopped roaring, and said softly, "Hello, what are you doing?" Dino and the hipposaur drank together at the water hole, then went for a walk in the sun.

▶ This activity will help your child to read a story, then compare preferences and common themes.

▶ Ask them to identify the common theme, then to write about which story they prefer, and why.

2. The children in Miss Grayson's class were sad because their teacher had gone home ill. They knew they would have a new teacher after lunch but didn't know who it was going to be. "I hope it's someone nice," said Clifton. "I hope it's someone fun," said Charlie. At the end of play, the class went into

the classroom and saw the most amazing thing sitting in Miss Grayson's chair. It was huge (as high as the roof), red, with eyes as big as a table. Then it spoke. "My name is Chris the Crocosaur, and I'm going to be your teacher this afternoon." The children giggled. "This is going to be fun," whispered Charlie. After the register, the children spent the afternoon painting dinosaurs and writing dinosaur stories.

Reading poems

Read these poems. They are both about the same thing!

1. Spaghetti for tea!
   Oh no, not again!
   My dad cooks it for me,
   but I hate it really.
   It's food for babies,
   all those **a**s, **b**s and **c**s.
   I prefer eating sausage
   with cabbage and peas.

This is about: _____

It is/is not my favourite because: _____

_____

_____

_____

This activity will help your child understand that different poems can have similar themes.

Ask them to say what the theme of each poem is, then to write about which one is their favourite and least favourite, and why.

Parents

46

2. I'd eat spaghetti for breakfast,
   and for dinner, and for tea.
   I would eat it at morning play, too,
   if it was left up to me.

This is about: _____

It is/is not my favourite because: _____

_____

_____

Reading rhymes

Read these rhymes.

1. There was an old woman
who lived in a shoe.
She had so many children she didn't
know what to do.
She gave them some broth without
any bread.
She spanked them all soundly and
put them to bed.

This is about: _____

It is/is not my favourite because:

_____

_____

_____

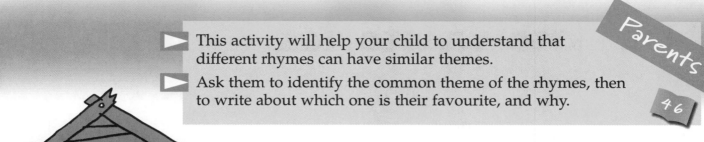

This activity will help your child to understand that different rhymes can have similar themes.

Ask them to identify the common theme of the rhymes, then to write about which one is their favourite, and why.

Parents

46

2. There was a crooked man, and
he walked a crooked mile.
He found a crooked sixpence against a crooked stile;
he bought a crooked cat, which caught a crooked mouse,
    and they all lived together in a little crooked house.

This is about: ─────────────────────────

It is/is not my favourite because:

_____

_____

_____

Well-known stories

Read this part of the story about Hansel and Gretel.

This activity will help your child to learn how to use a text to find the answers to questions.

Make sure they are familiar with this well-known story before they begin.

Parents

46

Hansel and Gretel had been lost in the forest all night and they were far away from home. Then Hansel saw a house. The two children went closer to see if they could see anyone. "Look," said Gretel. "It's a house made of sweets and gingerbread!" They pulled bits off the house to see what it tasted like. First they ate the letterbox. "Mmmm," said Hansel. Then they ate the top of the window. "Yummy," said Gretel. Just then, an old lady opened the front door. The children jumped back from the window to look at her. The lady was dressed in black and had very wrinkly skin, and a long wrinkly nose. Gretel could see she even had hairs in her chin. Her eyes were tiny. She looked like a witch. The lady spoke. "What are you doing here?" she asked them, in her strange voice. Hansel and Gretel were frightened...

Now answer these questions.

1. What was the house made from?

_____

2. Who saw the house first?

_____

3. Which part of the house did they eat first?

_____

4. What did the old lady look like?

_____

5. Where did Hansel and Gretel get lost?

_____

Reading non-fiction

Read what Siân has written about her dog, Cassie.

Cassie has lived with my family for three years. We chose her from the dogs' home when she was a puppy. We put a collar on Cassie with our telephone number and address on it in case she gets lost. Cassie eats one tin of dog food a day, and we give her our leftovers from tea as well. She loves it when we take her for a walk in the park. She tries to catch the rabbits, but they always run away from her. Cassie sleeps downstairs at night, in her basket.

Now draw and write about a pet you know.

31

What a lot of information!

Read this page from a newspaper.

Floods in Pontyvale

A police helicopter takes children away from the school.

Sports Centre

Supermarket!

Bread Frank's Fruit! Flowers

Pontyvale School

The sports centre is the only dry place in Pontyvale.

► This activity will help your child to understand the features of non-fiction texts including the layout of a page, how pictures are used, and how pictures are labelled.

Parents

46

Floodwater hit Pontyvale, Wales, last night after twenty centimetres of rain fell in one hour. People put bags of sand on their doorsteps to stop the water getting into their houses, and took furniture upstairs to keep it dry. But they had to leave their homes as rainwater came in through doors and downstairs windows. The police and fire brigade took some people to the sports centre, in rowing boats and speed boats. Children at Pontyvale school had to go onto the roof so that a police helicopter could lift them home to safety. The water is now one metre deep, and may get deeper!

Answer these questions.

1. What did people do to stop the water getting into their homes?

_____

2. Where did they put their furniture?

_____

3. How did the children get home from school?

_____

4. How did people get to the sports centre?

_____

5. How deep is the water in Pontyvale?

_____

What's missing?

Read these sentences to work out what is missing.
Use the words in the box to help.

This activity will help your child to read high frequency words on sight.

Ask them to read the possible answers first. Then to read each sentence, leaving the gap. Then to suggest the missing word.

people	more	four	water	will	house	school
half	time	half	many	would	tree	want

5

Do you want to come over to my _____ after _____?

6

_____ you like some _____ cake?

7

There are _____ apples on that _____, and I _____ the biggest one.

8

Is it _____ to go to school?

Find the word

Read these sentences. Choose a word from the box to fill the gaps. The first has been done for you.

1

Next week I am going on holiday.

2

_____ time is it?

3

At _____ today, I did drawing and writing.

4

I _____ my dog.

This activity will help your child to read high frequency words on sight.

Ask them to read each whole sentence first, to help them work out the missing word.

because ball three sister's school love made what ~~next~~

5

Please can we have our _____ back?

6

I want to go to sleep _____ I am tired.

7

_____ of us are dancing.

8

I have _____ a cake for my _____ birthday.

Which word fits?

Read this story and think of some of your own words that fit into the gaps. Use the words in the box to help, if you need to.

enormous	terrible	scary	ugly	shaky	silly
dizzy	laughed	smiled	giggled	pushed	fought

1. The _____ octopus jumped out of the sea and attacked the sailor.

2. The sailor _____ the _____ octopus off.

This activity will help your child to identify a range of words that might fit into a sentence.

Ask them to read the story first, then to suggest their own words that would make sense, perhaps from the box.

Parents

47

3. The octopus fell onto his head and felt _____ .

4. The sailor _____ then threw the octopus into the sea and sailed away.

Reading for sense

Read these sentences and circle the wrong word. The rewrite each one so it makes sense.

1. My cat was hungry so I gave him some flowers to eat.

_____

_____

2. When Humpty Dumpty fell off the wall, all the King's chairs came to mend him.

_____

_____

3. Little Miss Muffet, sat on her tuffet, eating some blocks of wood.

_____

_____

4. I took my dog for a walk in the bath.

_____

_____

► This activity will enable your child to check for sense when they are reading, and to suggest words that fit which would make an appropriate alternative.

Parents

47

5. 1, 2, 3, 4, 5, once I caught a car alive.
   6, 7, 8, 9, 10, then I put it back again.

_____

_____

6. The wolf said the three little pigs, "I'll huff and I'll puff, and I'll tap your house down."

_____

_____

_____

7. I put my goldfish in a plant pot.

_____

_____

8. My pet hamster loves running around his cabbage.

_____

_____

Words inside words

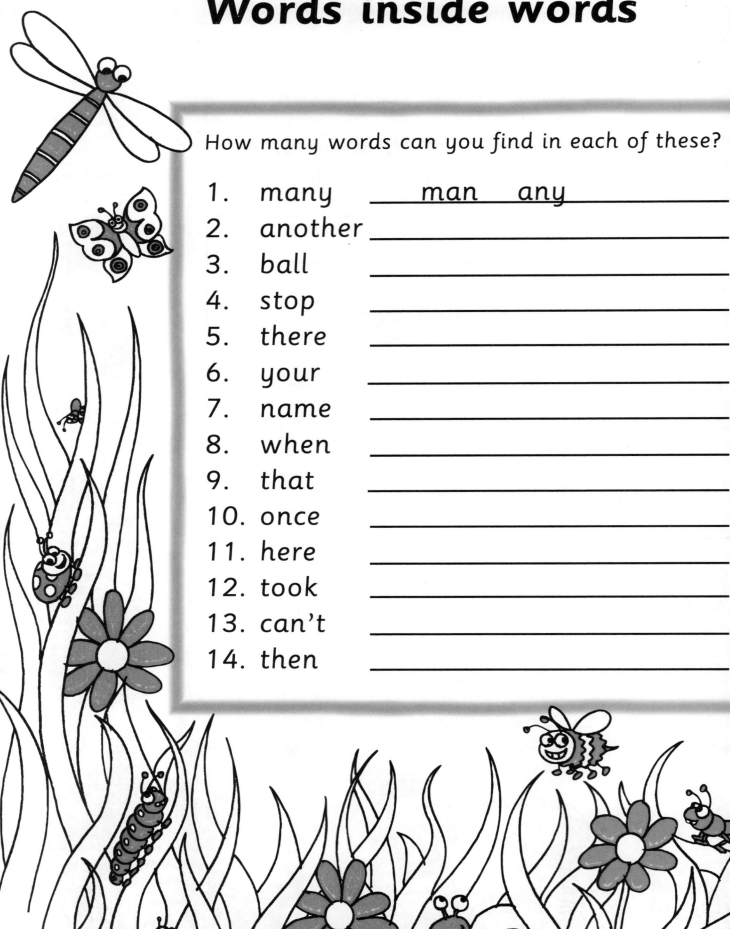

How many words can you find in each of these?

1. many   <u>man   any</u>
2. another _____
3. ball _____
4. stop _____
5. there _____
6. your _____
7. name _____
8. when _____
9. that _____
10. once _____
11. here _____
12. took _____
13. can't _____
14. then _____

This activity will help your child to recognise words within words.

Ask them to write every word within each word they can find.

15. brother _____

16. where _____

17. what _____

18. want _____

19. hope _____

20. smile _____

21. every _____

22. flower _____

23. season _____

24. banana _____

25. peace _____

26. mouse _____

27. window _____

28. plate _____

Further activities

4-5

▶ Although there are question words such as 'who', 'why', 'what', 'where', 'when', 'how' and 'do', sometimes these words are also used in normal sentences, or answers. For example, 'When we get to school, we will see our friends'. It's important, therefore, that children know what makes a question, other than these clue words, perhaps by asking someone for more information.

▶ Ask them to think of a question using each word, then to think of a sentence using each word. ('How do we get there?' 'That's how we get there'.)

▶ *Answers: 1, 2, 4, 5, 7, 8, 10, 11 and 12 are all questions and need a question mark. 3 and 9 need full stops and 6 can have a full stop or a question mark.*

6-7

▶ Ask your child to write number words when they are writing a story. Look for them elsewhere – in stories and number poems, for example.

▶ Encourage them to think of reasons why shops and

supermarkets use numbers rather than number words on displays and prices on products (they are more eye-catching, and take up less space).

▶ *Answers: twenty, nineteen, eighteen, seventeen, sixteen, fifteen, fourteen, thirteen, twelve, eleven, ten, nine, eight, seven, six, five, four, three, two, one, zero.*

8-9

▶ Write some colour labels on separate pieces of card for your child to read. Then ask them to match each word to a real object, or to a picture of a coloured object. (This is a good way of checking that your child can recognise colours as well as words – children who are colour-blind tend to confuse green and brown.)

▶ Look for colour stories, so they can practise

reading more colour words.

▶ *Answers: Your child can use any colours, as long as they make sense., for example 4 – brown, 5 – green plant, 7 – white or grey clouds, blue sky.*

10-11

▶ Make sure your child knows the correct order of the days of the week. Say them aloud together, often. Then write the each day of the week onto a separate piece of card, and ask your child to put them into the correct order.

▶ *Answers: It doesn't matter if your child uses full sentences or not, or if they speak or write the answers, so long as they are able to find each answer themselves. 1. To her Nan and grandad's house in Liverpool. 2. Her dad, 3. Swimming and Brownies, 4. It's her mum and dad's tenth wedding anniversary. 5. Rachel, 6. Sunday, 7. Saturday, 8. Four.*

12-13

▶ Ask your child to draw a plan of a place they know very well (perhaps their garden or their school playground), and to label parts of it. Allow them to use a word and picture dictionary to look up any words they find tricky.

▶ *Answers: Encourage your child to give as much detail as possible. 1. On Moon Road, just past South Street.*

2. The park and a church.
3. Sunny Road.
4. Park Road and East Street

▶ Ask your child to say which book is fiction (*Digger Dan*), and which book is non-fiction (*100 Space Songs*). Look at some more book covers in shops and libraries, and ask them to say what they think the book is about. Then open the book to check whether or not their prediction was correct.

▶ Look at a selection of non-fiction books (songs, encyclopaedias, atlases, dictionaries, history books, and other reference books), and fiction books (stories and poems) to make sure your child understands the difference.

▶ Encourage your child to look for other information given on the front and back cover of real books (for example, the price and a picture of the writer).

▶ Suggest they make a book cover for a story they have written, for a collection of family recipes, or for a scrapbook of photographs.

▶ Tell your child that blurb means information about a book which tells the reader about what type of book it is.

▶ Extend this activity further by asking your child to say what they think will happen next, or to talk about what they thought happened just before this part of each story.

▶ Ask them to talk about other stories they have read where the characters are scared, angry, jealous or happy, and to look for language in stories that tells them this. For example, we know

Cinderella was sad because 'a tear has just landed on her cheek'.

▶ Make sure your child reads stories with a variety of settings, for example, stories about imaginary lands, fantasy worlds or traditional places, home or school.

▶ Ask them to draw a picture of their favourite place in a story, perhaps grandma's cottage in *Little Red Riding Hood*, and to say or write why it is their favourite place.

▶ Ensure your child has access to stories with common themes, for example, stories about kings, and stories about children living in a variety of cultures.

▶ Borrow taped stories from your local library for them to listen to, and always ask them what they think about a story, to avoid them getting into the habit of saying 'I don't know'.

▶ To broaden this, ask their opinion on television programmes, music, dance and art.

Further activities

24-25

▶ Help your child to read the poems on this page with expression, reading with the exclamation marks, full stops and commas in the right places.

▶ Look for other poems or rhymes which have a food theme, such as *Five currant buns in a baker's shop*.

▶ To develop this idea, ask them to write poems about their favourite subject, perhaps, football, then to put them together in a scrapbook with a front and back cover for their book.

26-27

▶ Encourage your child to think of other rhymes which have similar themes, for example, *Twinkle twinkle little star* and *Hey diddle diddle* – both of which feature the sky at night.

▶ There are words in rhymes which your child may not understand, so underline them and talk about what they mean, for example, 'broth', 'spanked', 'crooked', 'mile', 'sixpence' and 'stile' which appear in the rhymes on this page.

28-29

▶ Read the full story of *Hansel and Gretel*, and ask your child more questions about what happened before the stepmother left them in the forest.

▶ To extend this activity further, find a recipe to make sweets or gingerbread biscuits.

▶ Talk to your child about the danger of talking to strangers, and what to do if they get lost.

▶ *Answers: 1. sweets and gingerbread; 2. Hansel; 3. the letterbox; 4. she was dressed in black, with wrinkly skin, a long wrinkly nose, hairs on her chin and tiny eyes; 5. in the forest.*

30-31

▶ Ask your child to read non-fiction books to find out more information about pets and to see how other non-fiction books are set out.

▶ Then ask them to make a book about their favourite pet or animal. See if they can divide the book into themed sections, with a contents page at the beginning. Include, for example,

sections on pet food, pet health and pet exercise. Then help them to write an information book about themselves. Ask what sections they would include, such as, my family, my hobbies, my school, my friends.

32-33

▶ Help your child to write a newspaper page about 'A day in my life' and ask them to include a picture or photograph with labels, and a few lines of writing.

▶ Give your child the experience of reading non-fiction books aimed at five- to six-year-olds (dictionaries, atlases, encyclopaedias, books about people and their jobs, people in history, famous

people, and people who live in other parts of the world).

▶ *Answers: 1. They put bags of sand on their doorsteps. 2. Upstairs 3. By police helicopter. 4. By rowing boat or speed boat. 5. One metre deep.*

▶ Block out some words in an unfamiliar story, one or two on each page, before your child starts to read it. Ask them to guess what each of the missing words are by reading the other words in the sentence around it first.

▶ If they cannot reach a word in a sentence, teach them to read the whole sentence, which puts the word into context.

▶ *Answers: 1. Who will be my partner? 2. Half for you, half for me. 3. Do you want to play with the water? 4. Are there too many people in this boat? 5. Do you want to come over to my house after school? 6. Would you like some more cake? 7. There are four apples on that tree, and I want the biggest one. 8. Is it time to go to school?*

▶ To extend this activity further, give your child a sentence and ask them to suggest alternative words. For example, 'The animal (new word) was big (new word)'.

▶ Try this with stories that are both familiar and unfamiliar to your child.

▶ *Answers: 2. What time is it? 3. At school today, I did drawing and writing. 4. I love my dog. 5. Please can we have our ball back? 6. I want to go to sleep because I am tired. 7. Three of us are dancing. 8. I have made a cake for my sister's birthday.*

▶ Sometimes when children read, they say a word that makes sense with the story but isn't the word actually written down in the sentence. Praise them when they do this, but don't be afraid to ask them to go back and try reading the word again.

▶ *Answers: Answers may vary.*

▶ Write more nonsense sentences for your child to read and spot the mistake. Then ask them to write some nonsense sentences.

▶ Play this as a game verbally, too, for example, 'Let's go into the garden and plant some pencils'.

▶ *Answers: The nonsense words are 1. flowers should be food; 2. chairs should be horses or men; 3. blocks of wood should be curds and whey; 4. bath should be park 5. car should be fish; 6. tap should be blow; 7. plant pot should be goldfish bowl; 8. cabbage should be wheel. There are many alternative solutions.*

▶ To extend this activity further, ask your child to make more words by moving the letters around, for example, 'brother' – 'hot', 'rot'.

▶ Then write some longer words for them to read and make words from, such as 'elephant', 'alligator' and so on.

▶ *Answers: 2. an, other; 3. all; 4. top; 5. the, here, her; 6. you our; 7. am; 8. hen; 9. hat, at; 10. on; 11. he, her; 12. too, to; 13. can; 14. the, he, hen; 15. other, rot, he, her; 16. here, he, her; 17. hat, at; 18. ant, an; 19. hop; 20. mile; 21. ever, eve, very; 22. flow, low, owe; 23. sea, son, on; 24. ban, an; 25. pea, ace; 26. use; 27. win, wind, do; 28. late, ate. Answers may vary.*

Celebration!

You are so clever!
Colour the stars to show
what you can do!

I can read and write numbers from zero to twenty.

I can read and write ten different names.

I can read stories, poems and rhymes.